THE GREAT BIG BOOK OF AMAZING ME

igl_oobooks

Published in 2021
First published in the UK by Igloo Books Ltd
An imprint of Igloo Books Ltd
Cottage Farm, NN6 0BJ, UK
Owned by Bonnier Books
Sveavägen 56, Stockholm, Sweden
www.igloobooks.com

0821 001
2 4 6 8 10 9 7 5 3 1
ISBN 978-1-80022-459-9

Designed by Simon Parker
Edited by Hannah Cather

Printed and manufactured in China

This journal belongs to:

⸺⸺⸺ *Aggie* ⸺⸺⸺

INTRODUCTION:

YOU ARE AMAZING. THAT'S A FACT.

SOMETIMES, THOUGH, WHEN LIFE GETS A BIT OVERWHELMING, IT CAN BE HARD
TO REMEMBER ALL THE REASONS WHY YOU ARE SO VERY, VERY AMAZING.
THIS JOURNAL IS A REMINDER OF THOSE REASONS, AS WELL AS MAKING YOU THINK ABOUT ALL
THE OTHER AMAZING THINGS IN YOUR LIFE – LOVED ONES, HOBBIES, TRAVELS, ADVENTURES, GOOD
MEMORIES, EXCITING FUTURE PLANS, DELICIOUS FOODS AND MORE. IT'S A DIP-IN, DIP-OUT, GUIDED
JOURNAL FOR YOU TO FILL IN AT YOUR LEISURE, WITH A FOCUS ON SELF-LOVE AND SELF-CARE.

SO, WHAT'S STOPPING YOU? GET STARTED AND DELVE RIGHT INTO THE GREAT BIG BOOK
OF AMAZING ME – WELL, YOU, BUT YOU KNOW WHAT WE MEAN.

HOW TO USE THIS JOURNAL:

INSIDE YOU'LL FIND A SERIES OF PROMPT QUESTIONS AND CREATIVE EXERCISES TO HELP YOU REFLECT ON WHAT MAKES YOU SO AMAZING. USING THIS JOURNAL IS THE PERFECT WAY TO CELEBRATE ALL THE AMAZING THINGS IN YOUR LIFE AND FIND OUT MORE ABOUT YOURSELF.

YOU MAY WISH TO WORK THROUGH THE JOURNALING PROCESS FROM BEGINNING TO END. OR YOU MAY PREFER TO FLIP TO A RANDOM PAGE AND START THERE — IT'S UP TO YOU.

IT'S IMPORTANT TO HAVE A CLEAR AND FOCUSED MIND WHEN JOURNALING, SO BE SURE TO FIND A QUIET PLACE THAT'S FREE FROM DISTRACTIONS. START WITH A POSITIVE ATTITUDE AND DON'T BE AFRAID TO HAVE FUN ALONG THE WAY!

I AM
POWERFUL,
BRILLIANT
&BRAVE.

THREE REASONS WHY YOU'RE POWERFUL:

hise

cined

gortgenk

THREE REASONS WHY YOU'RE BRILLIANT:

coal

THREE REASONS WHY YOU'RE BRAVE:

DON'T LIMIT YOURSELF TO THREE FOR EACH THOUGH. DO MORE! WRITE THEM BELOW:

YOU COULD USE THESE REASONS AS AFFIRMATIONS TO REMIND YOU OF YOUR AMAZINGNESS THROUGHOUT THE DAY, TOO.

1 ....

2 ....

3 ....

4 ....

5 ....

WRITE DOWN FIVE THINGS YOU LOVE ABOUT YOURSELF. IT COULD BE ABOUT YOUR PERSONALITY OR YOUR ATTRIBUTES, YOUR APPEARANCE OR YOUR SKILLS.

WAS IT EASY OR HARD TO THINK ABOUT WHY YOU LOVE YOURSELF?

WHY IS IT IMPORTANT TO LOVE YOURSELF?

·······································

NOW WRITE DOWN ONE THING THAT MAKES YOU AMAZING, BECAUSE YOU ARE AMAZING! THEN DRAW A SKETCH OF YOURSELF DOING THAT THING.

Imagine going for a walk in a special place...

Where are you?

....

What can you see?

....

What makes it so special?

....

When were you last there?

....

When will you go again?

....

Draw a little sketch of one of the views:

Decorate some stones with Kind messages and mantras, using paint.

Things to write on your stone: E.g. Today is a good day!

....
....
....
....
....

Place the finished stone in your garden, or somewhere for someone else to find, like the park.

Places to put your stone:

....
....
....
....
....

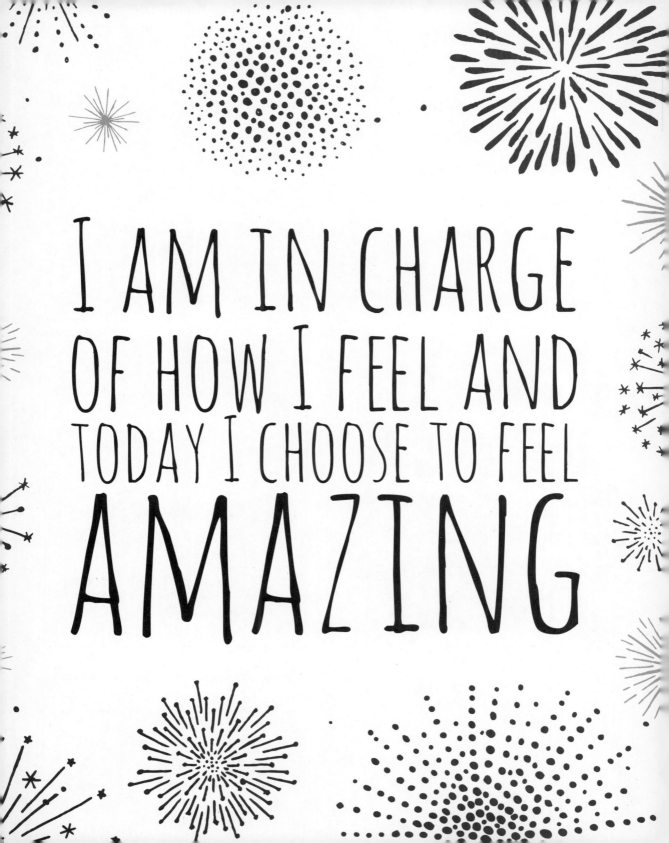

DAILY PLANNER

6AM

7AM

8AM

9AM

10AM

11AM

12PM

1PM

2PM

3PM

4PM

5PM

6PM

7PM

8PM

9PM

10PM

Plan out your day above and schedule in lots of little activities that make you feel amazing, like drinking a cup of tea, having a bath or going for a long walk with a friend. Big or small, there are lots of different ways to make today truly amazing.

Set a 60-second timer on your phone and write down as many Positive words as you can think of. Scribble them down anywhere and fill up the page as much as possible!

Use words from your scribbling session to create some affirmations for yourself. Make sure to write in the present tense, to be in the moment with your affirmation.

_____

_____

_____

_____

Do affirmations work for you? Plan times of the day when you will use them.

WRITE DOWN FIVE ACTS OF KINDNESS BELOW AND WHEN YOU'RE GOING TO DO THEM.

HOW ABOUT "PAY SOMEONE A COMPLIMENT" OR "SMILE AT A STRANGER"?

HOW DOES IT MAKE YOU FEEL TO DO NICE THINGS FOR OTHER PEOPLE?

....

....

SPREAD JOY

Fill the jar below with people's reactions to your kindness.
Were they happy? Surprised? Emotional?

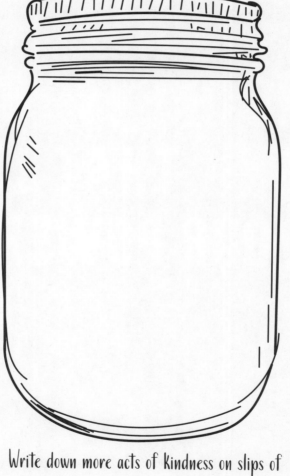

Write down more acts of kindness on slips of
paper and place them, folded, into a real jar.
Pick one out daily and try to achieve it!

"NO ONE IS YOU, AND THAT IS YOUR POWER."

On a scale of 1-10, how powerful do you feel now?

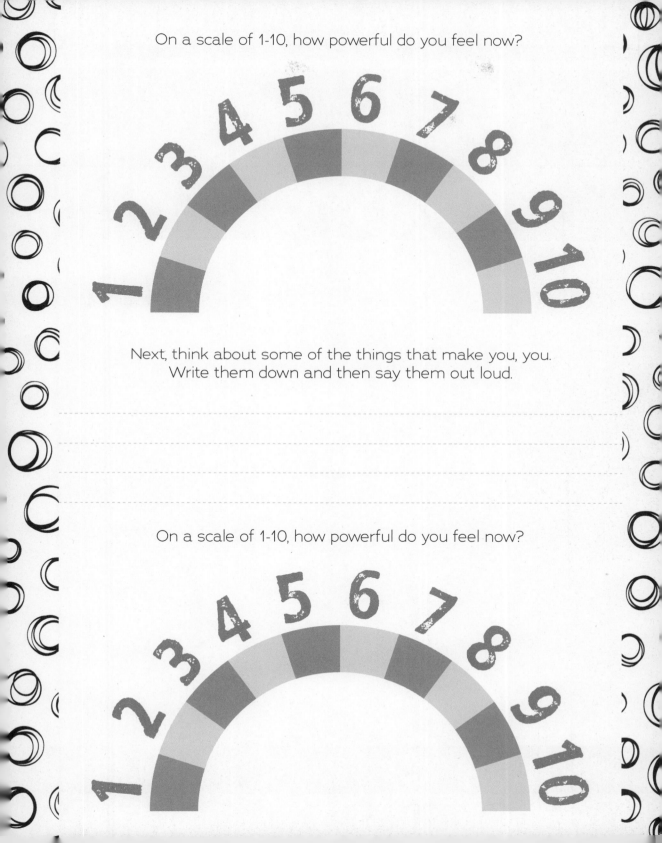

Next, think about some of the things that make you, you.
Write them down and then say them out loud.

On a scale of 1-10, how powerful do you feel now?

CLOSE YOUR EYES AND IMAGINE THAT YOU ARE ON A BEAUTIFUL BEACH AT SUNSET.

WHAT KIND OF THINGS CAN YOU SEE, HEAR AND TOUCH?
TAKE A MOMENT AND SIT WITH THIS THOUGHT.

SKETCH OUT THE SCENE ABOVE, WITH LITTLE NOTES AND THOUGHTS AROUND IT.

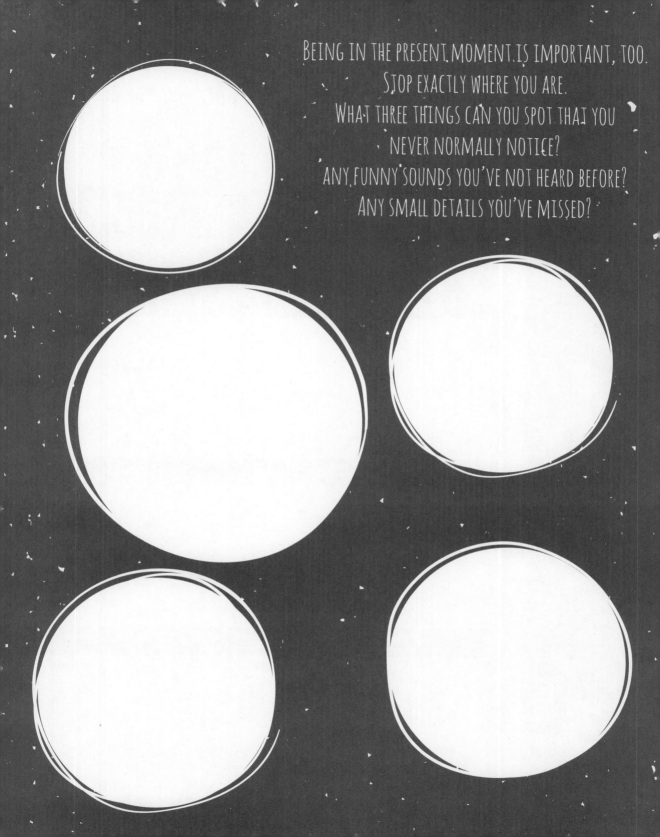

Being in the present moment is important, too.
Stop exactly where you are.
What three things can you spot that you
never normally notice?
Any funny sounds you've not heard before?
Any small details you've missed?

WRITE DOWN THREE FLAWS YOU THINK YOU HAVE.

THEN, WRITE DOWN HOW YOU CAN MAKE THE BEST OF THAT FLAW.

FOR EXAMPLE:

I worry too much...
... but worrying means I care about things.

I go to bed too late...
... but that means I enjoy finding things to do.

FLAWS ARE PART OF BEING HUMAN. TO CELEBRATE OUR FLAWS, WRITE "I LOVE ME FOR ME" AS BIG AS YOU CAN ON THIS PAGE AND DECORATE EACH LETTER.

CAN YOU ACCEPT YOUR FLAWS AS PART OF YOU BEING YOU?

MY LIST

WRITE A TO-DO LIST OF ALL THE JOBS YOU NEED TO DO, BIG OR SMALL.

NOW, WRITE DOWN SOME JOBS THAT ARE ALL ABOUT SELF-CARE AND PUT THEM INTO YOUR MAIN TO-DO LIST. PLACE SOME AT THE TOP!

Write down items that bring you joy but also start with the first initial of your name. Think of as many as you can!

If you're struggling to fill the page, use the first letter of your last name, too!

Food Fuel

Use the bubbles below to write down six of your best-loved foods, drinks or meals, and then explain why they made the shortlist.

Mindful eating tip:
Remember to put down your knife and fork in between mouthfuls, to enjoy each tasty moment.

Think back on the previous
week and note down a few
things you are grateful for.
They could be people,
events or animals.

Sketch out three thank you notes to anyone in your life. Write down a little message, explaining what you're grateful for and why. Include one for yourself!

You've survived **100%** of your worst days. You can do the same again.

THINK ABOUT ONE OF YOUR WORST DAYS.
WHAT HAPPENED? HOW DID IT FEEL?

THEN REALIZE THAT YOU GOT THROUGH THOSE BAD DAYS. YOU LEARNED A LESSON AND YOU CAME OUT THE OTHER SIDE, SO YOU CAN DO IT AGAIN AND AGAIN!

NOTE DOWN ALL THE REASONS
WHY YOU DESERVE A TREAT:

HOW OFTEN DO YOU TREAT YOURSELF?

CREATE A TREAT-YOURSELF CHECKLIST BELOW. IT MIGHT INCLUDE TAKING A BUBBLE BATH OR BUYING A NEW TOP. MAKE SURE TO CHECK THEM OFF ASAP!

HOW DOES TREATING YOURSELF MAKE YOU FEEL?

YOU ARE AMAZING IN SO MANY DIFFERENT WAYS.

DESIGN YOUR SUPERHERO OUTFIT BELOW. WHICH SUPERPOWERS WOULD YOU HAVE?

YOU ARE A SUPERHERO!

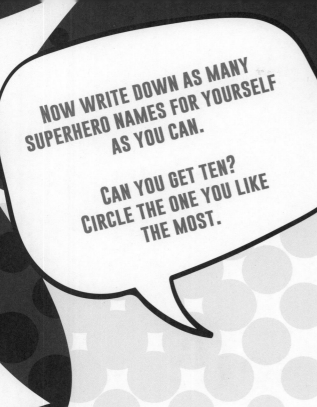

Note to self:

I am enough.

**FILL THIS PAGE WITH NOTES ON THE IDEA OF
"BEING ENOUGH" AND WHETHER YOU FEEL THIS WAY.
IF NOT, HOW COULD YOU CHANGE IT?**

DRAW SOME OF YOUR BEST-LOVED MEMORIES FROM THIS YEAR AS A POLAROID PICTURE.

Are they with friends or family? Where are they? What made them a special memory for you?

PLAN OUT SOME MEMORY-MAKING ADVENTURES BELOW. THEY COULD BE BIG TRIPS TO FAR-OFF PLACES OR AS SIMPLE AS A SUNNY AFTERNOON IN THE PARK.

Where are you heading first?

What will you do when you're there?

Who is with you?

How would you travel there?

Imagine a big fridge, stocked with all kinds of delicious food. It's really full! Which meals would you make?

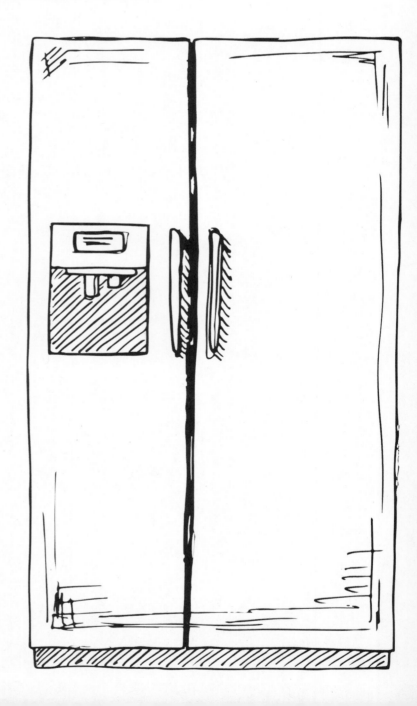

Design some fun fridge magnets,
with quotes and images that inspire you.
You might want to draw loved ones, or
write your name or a special phrase.

SHOPPING LIST

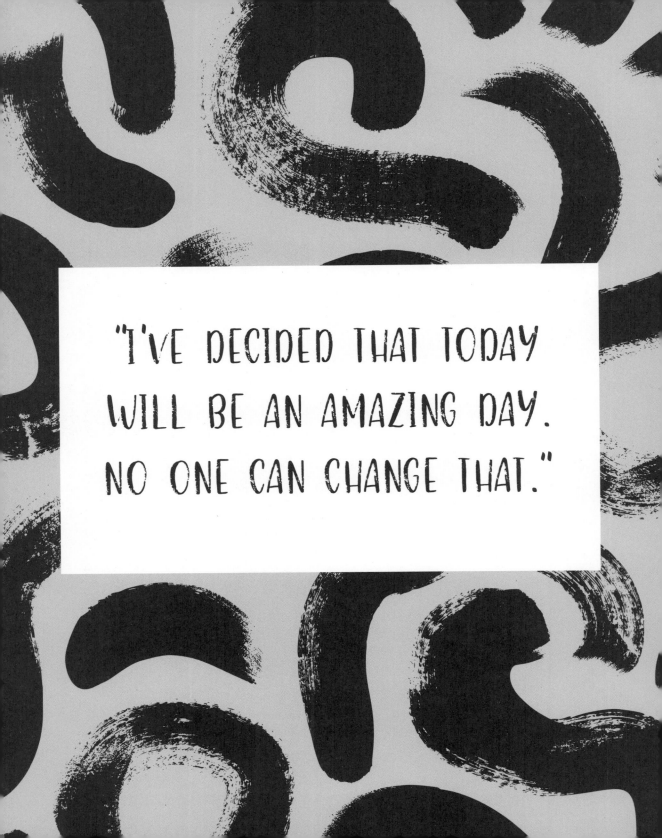

Your friend cancels your plans – are you annoyed, or do you choose to let go and make the most of the day?

If someone is not very nice to you – do you choose to be sad, or let go and continue to be happy?

Choosing to let go can be hard, but it is freeing. Make some notes below on letting go. Are you able to do it, or do you tend to hold onto things? Who does it serve?

DESIGN A PLAYLIST FOR YOUR DAY.

_____

_____

_____

_____

_____

_____

◁◁　　　▷　　　▷▷

WHICH SONG WOULD BE THE BEST TO WAKE UP TO?

_____

WHICH SONG IS GOOD FOR WHEN YOU'RE ON THE MOVE?

_____

WHICH SONG GETS YOU TO SLEEP AT NIGHT?

_____

WHICH SONGS MAKE YOU SING OUT LOUD?

HOW DOES SINGING WITHOUT ANY INHIBITIONS MAKE YOU FEEL?

WHAT KIND OF DANCE MOVES CAN YOU DO?
SKETCH THEM BELOW.

PLACE YOUR HAND ON THE
OPPOSITE PAGE, DRAW AROUND
IT AND THEN DECORATE IT.
MAYBE YOU'RE INSPIRED BY INTRICATE
PATTERNS, OR MAYBE YOU COULD DRAW
ALL OF THE TATTOOS YOU'VE EVER
IMAGINED HAVING!

YOU COULD SKETCH
OUT HOW YOUR HAND
ACTUALLY LOOKS, WITH
FRECKLES, KNUCKLES
AND SPOTS, AND SEE
THE BEAUTY IN IT.

GET OUT OF YOUR OWN WAY.
DON'T LET You STOP
You FROM
Achieving.

DRAW A PATHWAY ALL AROUND THIS PAGE.
IT COULD BE WINDING AND LOOPING, OR
COMPLETELY STRAIGHT, THEN WRITE A GOAL YOU'D
LIKE TO ACHIEVE AT THE END OF THE PATH.

ARE THERE ANY OBSTACLES
THAT HOLD YOU BACK?
ARE YOU SCARED OR
WORRIED ABOUT
ANYTHING?
DRAW THEM IN.

HOW CAN YOU OVERCOME THE OBSTACLES IN YOUR PATH?

....

....

WHAT LESSONS CAN BE LEARNED FROM OVERCOMING OBSTACLES?

....

....

Pie Chart of Me

What different parts make up you?
Maybe you're 50% fun, 5% lazy, 20% sports-fanatic and 25% chocolate.
Break up the circle into different sections that represent you.

Now you've completed a pie chart of you, why not do one
for your life and how your time is divided? Include you, your family, work,
friends, sleep, and fun. Is your work/life balance in check?

My No-Social-Media Day

Plan a day with no social media and think of all you could do instead of spending time on your computer or phone. Write it all down below.

If a day seems a little daunting at first, perhaps try a morning or a specific number of hours.

Remember, though, that having a phone can bring lots of positive things to your life, too. It means you can call your grandma, reply to a post, or find a lovely gift for someone. Continue this list on this page.

MAKE THE REST OF YOUR LIFE, THE BEST OF YOUR LIFE.

Write down three life goals or dreams.

How are these goals going to make the rest of your life the best?

1.

2.

3.

....
....
....
....
....
....
....

What can you do to make sure these come true?

You are amazing and you deserve a treat!
Think about seven little gifts for yourself and
plan a week of treats below:

1.

2.

3.

4.

5.

6.

7.

These can be anything from taking time out to read your book or sleeping for an extra ten minutes, to buying chocolate!

Remember, though, that treats work both ways!
Write down three people in your life that deserve
to receive a treat, and why.

Then, think about a treat that they would love and write it down.
When are you going to give them these treats?

ME AND MY REFLECTION

Look at yourself in a mirror or take a selfie,

and then answer the following questions.

How do you feel when you look at your reflection?

....

....

What do you like about what you see?

....

....

What makes you amazing?

....

....

....

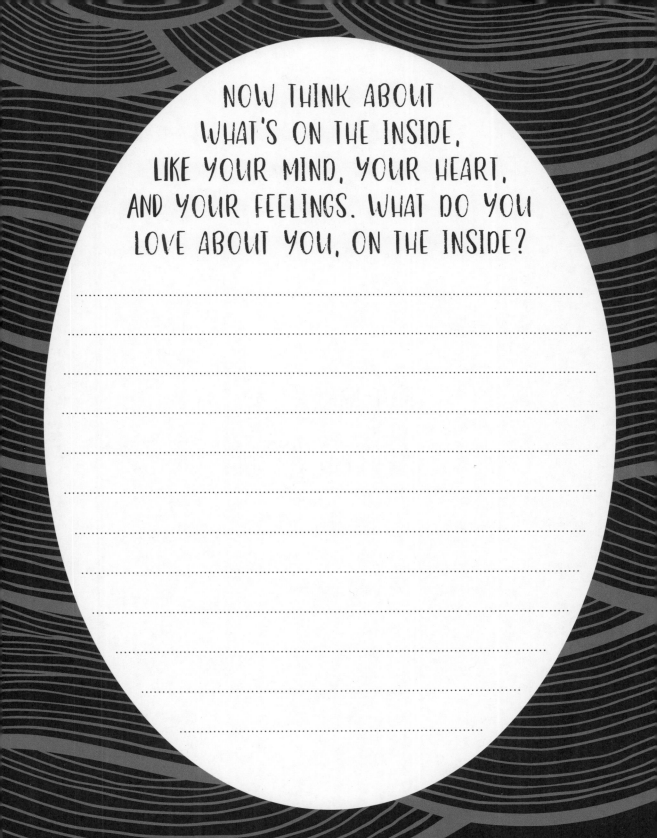

NOW THINK ABOUT
WHAT'S ON THE INSIDE,
LIKE YOUR MIND, YOUR HEART,
AND YOUR FEELINGS. WHAT DO YOU
LOVE ABOUT YOU, ON THE INSIDE?

Positive thoughts

What do you think about the quote on the opposite page? Try writing it down ten times on this page and then say it out loud ten times, too. How do you feel?

Affirmations are great for making you feel strong and loved. Try saying one every morning or right before bed and see if it helps you.

What other affirmations would be useful for you?

Concentrate on each of the letters below and write down a single word or phrase (that starts with that letter) about why you are so amazing.

A

M

A

Z

I

N

G

M

E

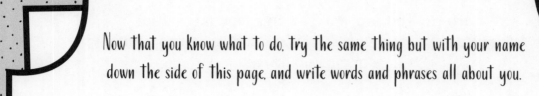

Now that you know what to do, try the same thing but with your name down the side of this page, and write words and phrases all about you.

Where do you see yourself this time next year?
Where do you see yourself in five and then ten years?
Make some notes!

Do you like thinking
about the future?
Is it good to plan
ahead?

Looking into the future is great, but it's also good to be in the moment. Draw or sketch yourself right now, wherever you are. Describe the situation and how you're feeling.

I am amazing.
True story.

Create a (very) short story below, all about you
doing something truly amazing. Maybe you could use
a real-life experience as inspiration.

What about setting? Characters? Dialogue?
Most importantly, what's the moral?

Write down three nice things your best friend

would say about you:

1

2

3

Which qualities do you think make you a good friend?

....

....

....

....

....

....

Now, speak to yourself like you are a parent.

What three pieces of advice would you give yourself?

1

2

3

Write down three nice things your family would say about you:

1

2

3

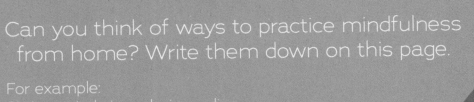

Can you think of ways to practice mindfulness from home? Write them down on this page.

For example:
Sitting quietly in a chair, reading.
Taking some peaceful moments to look out of the window.
Doing a DIY home yoga session.

Now think about ways to practice
mindfulness outside. Add to the list below:

Take a walk and notice what your senses pick up.

Sit in a park or your garden, close your eyes and listen to the birds.

Take deep breaths, in and out, of fresh outdoor air.

SELF-LOVE
IS NOT
SELFISH

Think about the quote on the previous page.
Remember that self-love is not selfish and
that it is, in fact, completely necessary.

Write down three ways
you can show self-love to
yourself today.
Make them a priority and
mark them off as
you do them.

1.
....

....

....

2.
....

....

....

3.
....

....

....

Being amazing all of the time is unrealistic and it's important to remember that it's okay to not be okay. There's plenty to learn from negative feelings. Complete the sentences below and you'll see how.

IT'S OKAY TO NOT BE OKAY BECAUSE...

....

....

IT'S OKAY TO BE ANGRY BECAUSE...

....

....

IT'S OKAY TO BE TIRED BECAUSE...

....

....

IT'S OKAY TO BE BORED BECAUSE...

....

....

Feelings go up and down and
that is completely normal.
Draw your own up-and-down
roller coaster of your weekly
emotions below and decorate.

IDEAL DINNER PARTY GUESTLIST? DISCUSS.

THERE CAN BE FIVE GUESTS BESIDES YOURSELF. WHO WOULD YOU INVITE? THEY CAN BE DEAD OR ALIVE, FAMOUS OR NOT FAMOUS. WHAT WOULD YOU TALK ABOUT? HOW WOULD THE EVENING GO? WHERE WOULD THE PARTY BE HELD?

WHAT WOULD BE ON THE MENU?
THINK OF ALL THE AMAZING MEALS YOU LOVE AND
THAT YOUR GUESTS WOULD LOVE.
DRAW OUT A LITTLE MENU PLAN ABOVE.
WHAT ABOUT DRINKS?

To fall in
Love
WITH YOURSELF
IS THE FIRST
SECRET
TO happiness

Think about your secrets. Are you quite a secretive person or do you share lots of things with people? Neither is right or wrong because everyone is different and deals with things in different ways.

What do you think are the secrets to happiness?

What do you think is the secret to an amazing life?

DRAW A CIRCLE BELOW.
THIS IS YOUR COMFORT ZONE.

Tthink about what should be inside of it
and doodle some notes and sketches.
What things are outside of your comfort zone?

WHY IS IT GOOD TO GO OUT OF YOUR
COMFORT ZONE SOMETIMES?

....

....

THIS PAGE IS FOR TAKING A BREAK.

No guidance. No direction. Just fill it in however you'd like.
Whether that's words or sketches, let your mind wander and doodle freely.

Red, Pink, Yellow, Green, Blue, White, Purple, Orange, Black.

WHICH ONE OF THE ABOVE REPRESENTS YOU? WHY?

WHICH OF THE ABOVE DO YOU ASSOCIATE WITH HAPPINESS? WHY?

WHICH OF THE ABOVE DO YOU ASSOCIATE WITH ANGER? WHY?

WHICH OF THE ABOVE DO YOU ASSOCIATE WITH CALM? WHY?

WHICH OF THE ABOVE DO YOU ASSOCIATE WITH FEELING AMAZING? WHY?

This page is a wall.
Create your own graffiti
design on it and decorate
it to the max!

BE YOURSELF. AN ORIGINAL IS SO MUCH BETTER THAN A COPY.

CAN YOU THINK OF ANY MOVIES OR SONGS THAT HAVE AN ORIGINAL AND A COPY?

Write them down below, and in each case, say which one you thought was better and why.

THE ORIGINAL YOU IS ALWAYS THE BEST ONE.

THINK ABOUT THE THREE THINGS IN YOUR LIFE THAT YOU ARE MOST PROUD OF ACHIEVING.

 1.

 **2.**

 3.

REMEMBER THAT THESE ARE ONLY VALID UP TO TODAY'S DATE.
THERE ARE SO MANY AMAZING THINGS TO ACHIEVE IN THE FUTURE!

Quick-fire questions:

Chocolate	or	**CHEESE?**
CITY	or	Country?
Bath	or	SHOWER?
Call	or	**TEXT?**
Book	or	MOVIE?
Summer	or	**WINTER?**

CREATE A LIST OF ACTIVITIES

The list should be full of crafts, games, walks,
fun tasks, trips and get-togethers. Don't forget
to add in at least two self-care activities!

TO-DO LIST:

DIY MEDITATION

Fill the page below with a description of a walk in a special place,
a stream of consciousness, or a gentle flow of positive messages.
This will create a homemade meditation that is specific to you.

LOVE YOURSELF AND THE
REST WILL FOLLOW

**DO YOU THINK THIS QUOTE IS TRUE?
LIST TEN DIFFERENT REASONS HOW
LOVING YOURSELF IS SUCH AN
IMPORTANT LOVE TO HAVE.**

1.

2.

3.

4.

5.

6.

7.

8.

9.

10.

WHO IS YOUR HERO?

Write their name down and then
draw a little portrait of them below.
You could Include yourself in the picture, too!

It could be someone famous that you've never met or someone in your family, or a friend.

What is it that makes them your hero?
Do you think you share any of these qualities?

Remember, though, that even heroes have weak spots. What is yours? and What can you do to work on your weak spot?

DESIGN YOUR DREAM HOUSE

LOCATION?

STYLE OF HOUSE?

NUMBER AND LAYOUT OF ROOMS?

SIZE?

EXTRA FEATURES?

DECORATION STYLE?

FURNITURE ESSENTIALS?

VIEWS?

DRAW A SKETCH OF YOUR DREAM HOUSE HERE:

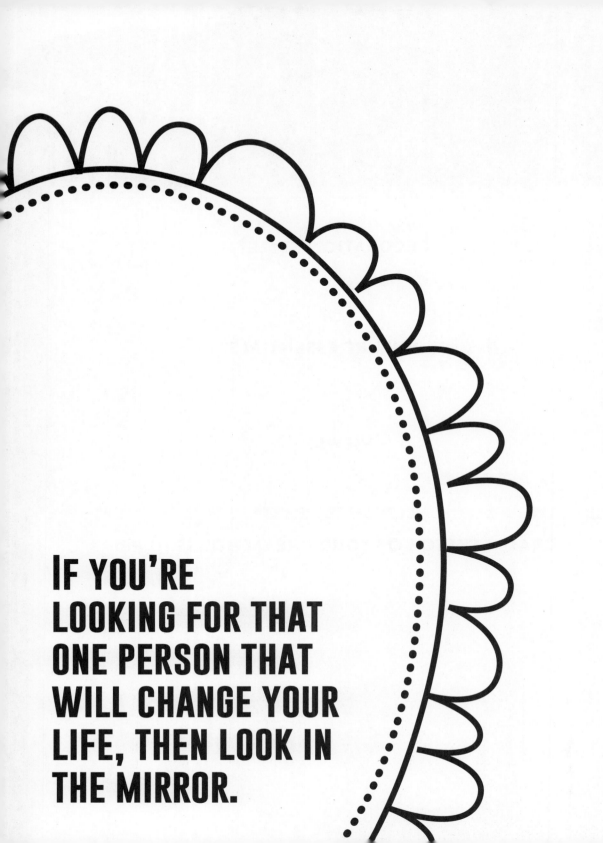

IF YOU'RE LOOKING FOR THAT ONE PERSON THAT WILL CHANGE YOUR LIFE, THEN LOOK IN THE MIRROR.

DRAW A HEAD-AND-SHOULDERS SHOT OF YOU BELOW.

WHAT KIND OF HAIRSTYLE DO YOU HAVE?

WHICH CLOTHES ARE YOU WEARING?

WHAT MAKES IT LOOK LIKE YOU?

Self-Care Bingo!
Cross off when you achieve any of the below,
and see if you can get a row, a column,
a diagonal line or a full house!

COOK YOUR FAVORITE MEAL	TELL YOURSELF SOMETHING YOU LOVE ABOUT YOURSELF	GIVE YOURSELF A TREAT
DO SOMETHING ONLY FOR YOU	NO SOCIAL MEDIA FOR AN HOUR BEFORE BEDTIME	GIVE YOURSELF A COMPLIMENT
GIVE YOURSELF A BIG SELF-HUG!	TAKE A BUBBLE BATH	HAVE A PAMPER EVENING

Describe your current self-care routine.
Do you have one? Self-care is about taking care
of yourself and showing self-kindness.

Then, describe the ultimate self-care routine for you,
to make you feel amazing. Plan in some time and ways
to make it achievable.

IMAGINE A RECIPE WHERE THE RESULT WOULD BE THE AMAZING YOU.

WHAT THINGS GO INTO MAKING YOU FEEL AMAZING?
WHAT ARE THE VITAL INGREDIENTS?
HOW MUCH OF THOSE INGREDIENTS NEED TO BE USED?
HOW MUCH PREPARATION TIME IS NEEDED?

WHAT DO YOU LOVE TO COOK?
NAME SOME BEST-LOVED MEALS:

PLAN IN AN AFTERNOON OF BAKING.
WHAT WOULD YOU LIKE TO MAKE?
WHO WITH?

MAKE SURE YOU REMEMBER TO HAVE
LOTS OF SAMPLES ALONG THE WAY!

THIS LIFE IS MINE ALONE.
SO I HAVE STOPPED ASKING PEOPLE FOR DIRECTIONS
TO PLACES THEY'VE NEVER BEEN.

— GLENNON DOYLE

WHICH DIRECTION ARE YOU GOING IN?

WHERE WOULD YOU LIKE YOUR LIFE TO GO?

WHAT ADVICE WOULD YOU GIVE TO YOURSELF

ON YOUR JOURNEY?

DESIGN YOURSELF AS A CARTOON. PICK OUT THREE UNIQUE FEATURES TO EXAGGERATE.

WHICH OUTFIT WOULD YOU CHOOSE TO WEAR?
HOW WOULD YOU STYLE YOUR HAIR?

CREATE A CARTOON WORLD FOR THE CARTOON YOU TO LIVE IN.

WHAT KIND OF SETTING IS IT?
WHAT ARE THE OTHER PEOPLE LIKE?

Look out of the nearest window and
list down the five nicest things you can see.

1

2

3

4

5

How does nature make you feel?

....

....

....

....

....

Use this page to sketch a lovely nature scene.
It might be in the woods, on, a beach, a hill or a riverside.
Which animals are present? What sounds can you hear?

Be your **own** reason to *smile*

WRITE DOWN FIVE JOKES TO TELL YOURSELF...

DRAW LOTS OF SMILING EMOJI FACES AROUND THE PAGE. THE BIGGER THE SMILE, THE BETTER!

THIS IS THE STAIRWAY TO FEELING AMAZING.

What five steps can you take today to make you feel incredible?

1.

2.

3.

4.

5.

FOR EXAMPLE, EATING A GOOD BREAKFAST MIGHT BE ONE STEP, AND CONNECTING WITH AN OLD FRIEND MIGHT BE ANOTHER.

How long do you think it will take you to achieve all five steps?

Describe feeling amazing.

Which words and images come to mind?

Why is feeling amazing so amazing?

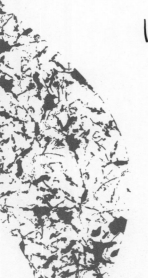

DO YOU LIKE TO READ?
WHICH CHARACTER FROM A BOOK ARE
YOU MOST LIKE AND WHY?
WHICH GENRE OF BOOK WOULD YOU BE AND WHY?

ANSWER THE QUESTIONS HERE:

WHAT ARE YOUR ALL-TIME BEST-LOVED BOOKS? IT MIGHT BE HARD TO CHOOSE, BUT TRY THREE FOR NOW!

1.

2.

3.

SET A 60-SECOND TIMER ON
YOUR PHONE AND WRITE DOWN
AS MANY HAPPY WORDS ON
THIS PAGE AS YOU CAN.

THEY MIGHT BE FEELINGS,
FOOD, QUOTES, FRIENDS .
ANYTHING THAT PUTS A BIG
HAPPY, AMAZING SMILE ON
YOUR FACE!

WHICH PHYSICAL ACTIVITY OR SPORT DO YOU MOST LOVE TO DO?

....

How often do you do it?

....

....

What do you get from doing it, mentally and physically?

....

....

How long have you done it for?

....

....

PLAN A FUN WORKOUT ROUTINE THAT WORKS FOR YOU:

What time will you start your workout?

....

Duration of your workout:

....

Which exercises or activities will you do?

....

....

What will be your treat afterward? Because you have to have a treat!

....

....

DRAW THE OUTLINE OF A PLAIN T-SHIRT BELOW. THEN, DESIGN A PATTERN ON IT, OR ADD A QUOTE, AN IMAGE, A SPECIAL NUMBER.

WOULD YOU WEAR
THIS T-SHIRT?

WHAT DO YOU THINK IS THE MOST IDEAL OUTFIT FOR:

A PARTY?

A CHILL BARBECUE?

A SUNDAY AT HOME?

A WALK OUTSIDE/ DOG WALK?

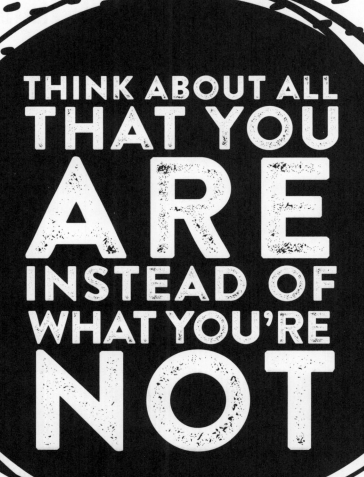

THINK ABOUT ALL THAT YOU ARE INSTEAD OF WHAT YOU'RE NOT

MAKING LISTS

Look at the two lists below.
Fill in the first list as much as you can,
with all the qualities and traits that make up you.
Then, look at the second list and write down all of
the good things you do in your life, including
hobbies or activities.

In an
ideal world...

What would your job be?

....

....

Which country would you live in?

....

....

What would you eat everyday?

....

....

What time would you get up, and go to bed?

....

....

In the real world...

WHAT THREE THINGS DO YOU LOVE?

....

....

....

WHICH THREE PEOPLE DO YOU LOVE?

....

....

....

WHAT ARE THREE OF YOUR UPCOMING PLANS?

....

....

....

WOULD YOU RATHER...

Be on vacation forever **OR** stay in one place forever?

Have five dogs as pets **OR** Have five cats as pets?

Be a superstar rock star **OR** bE a world-famous sports star?

Look amazing on the outside **OR** Feel amazing on the inside?

Hopefully the last choice is never an option!
you can be amazing on the outside and the inside all at
the same time!

List different ways to look after the ins and outs of you.

-
-
-
-
-
-
-
-

INVEST IN YOURSELF.
IT PAYS THE
BEST INTEREST.

DRAW YOURSELF IN THE MIDDLE OF THE PAGE. IT COULD BE CARTOON STYLE OR MORE REALISTIC, WHICHEVER YOU PREFER. THEN MAKE NOTES AROUND THE PICTURE ABOUT HOW YOU CAN INVEST IN YOURSELF. WHAT CAN YOU PUT IN AND GET OUT?

Which five songs have impacted your life the most so far?

1.

2.

3.

4.

5.

Why are each of those songs so special to you?
Are there memories attached to them?

Choose three of your best-loved songs. Write them down below and then add some more to make a feel-good playlist.

FREESTYLE DRAWING
FOR MINDFULNESS

First, draw tons of different shapes all over this page.
Then see what amazing things you can make from each shape.
Let your pen move smoothly and calmly around the page.

NOW, TRY FREESTYLE WRITING:

Starting with the prompt below, continue writing and don't stop until you reach the end of the page. Make sure you don't think about what's going onto the page. Just keep writing and see what comes to mind!

I am amazing because...

Believe you can

AND YOU'RE HALFWAY THERE

COMPLETE THESE SENTENCES...

I BELIEVE I CAN...

I BELIEVE I WILL...

I BELIEVE I AM ABLE TO...

I BELIEVE I SHOULD...

NOW MAKE THOSE THINGS HAPPEN.

DESIGN YOUR IDEAL OUTDOOR SPACE...

IS THERE GRASS? A SEATING AREA?
LOTS OF FLOWERS OR LOTS OF TREES?
POOL? BARBECUE?
WHAT MAKES IT IDEAL FOR YOU?

DOODLE ALL KINDS OF FLOWERS AND PLANTS BELOW.
REMEMBER TO TREAT YOURSELF LIKE A PLANT.
WATER YOURSELF WITH LOVE, CARE, FOOD AND WATER,
AND YOU WILL FLOURISH AND GROW.

HOW CAN YOU NOURISH YOURSELF?

LAUGHING OUT LOUD

THERE ARE SO MANY DIFFERENT WAYS TO LAUGH AND ALL OF THEM FEEL AMAZING!
FILL IN THE SPEECH BUBBLES BELOW WITH WAYS OF LAUGHING.

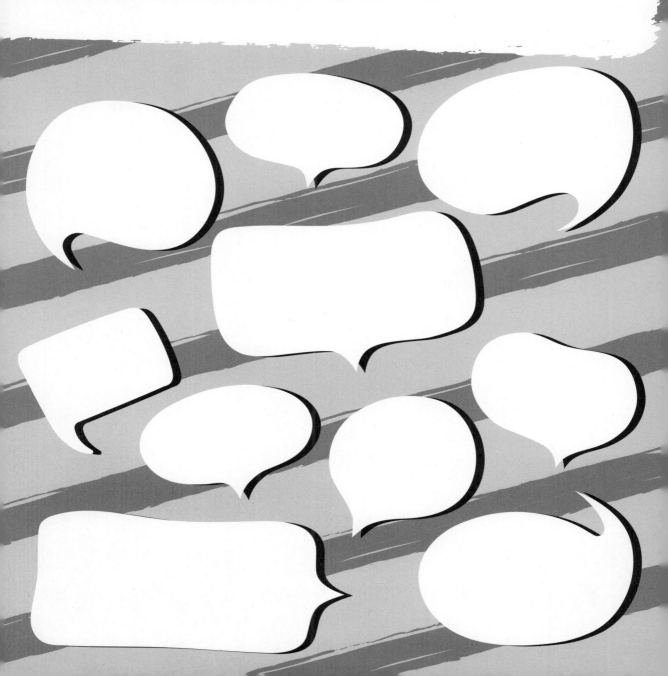

WRITE DOWN THREE JOKES.
REMEMBER THEM SO THAT YOU CAN
TELL THEM TO YOUR LOVED ONES.

1.

2.

3.

NOW, MAKE YOUR OWN UP! HOW ABOUT STARTING WITH
"KNOCK, KNOCK...", OR "WHAT DO YOU GET IF YOU CROSS A...?"

Self-confidence is
the best outfit.
Wear it and own it.

Design some outfits below.

Where would you wear each outfit?
What is the essential item that makes the outfit?

DRAW A CIRCLE WITH YOUR NAME IN THE MIDDLE OF IT.
NEXT, WRITE DOWN THE SPECIAL PEOPLE IN YOUR LIFE AROUND
THE CIRCLE — FRIENDS, FAMILY, COLLEAGUES.

DOES IT MAKE
YOU REALIZE HOW
SUPPORTED YOU ARE?
AND HOW MANY
AMAZING PEOPLE YOU
HAVE AROUND
YOU?

IMAGINE A DAY IN THE FUTURE WITH SOME OF THE SPECIAL PEOPLE YOU JUST MENTIONED. WHAT WOULD YOUR PLANS BE? WHERE WOULD YOU GO?

ROLL A DIE...

... and complete the task below that matches the rolled number.
Do it several more times until you've done each task at least once!

1. Say something amazing that happened yesterday.

2. Say something you learned recently.

3. Say something that's amazing about you.

4. Describe someone amazing in your life.

5. Say something you're looking forward to.

6. Give yourself a compliment.

NOW WRITE DOWN SIX JOBS YOU NEED TO GET DONE:

Roll a die and complete the job below that matches the rolled number.
Make sure to check off that you've completed the task!

1.

2.

3.

4.

5.

6.

YOU WERE BORN TO BE REAL, NOT PERFECT.

DO YOU THINK PERFECTION IS POSSIBLE?

WHAT CAN WE LEARN FROM ACCEPTING OUR IMPERFECTIONS?

WRITE DOWN TEN THINGS THAT YOU COULD BE DOING RATHER THAN STRIVING FOR PERFECTION:

1.

2.

3.

4.

5.

6.

7.

8.

9.

10.

MY BEST-EVER VACATION

DRAW A SCENE FROM IT BELOW:

WHAT MADE IT SO SPECIAL FOR YOU?

NOW THINK ABOUT YOUR TOP
BUCKET-LIST TRAVEL DESTINATIONS.
YOU MIGHT HAVE ONE OR MANY.
MAKE THE LIST BELOW.

WHO WOULD YOU LIKE TO TRAVEL WITH?

....

....

....

WHY DID YOU CHOOSE THOSE PLACES?

....

....

....

....

IMAGINE THERE IS AN
AWARDS CEREMONY ALL ABOUT
YOU AND YOU ARE THE WINNER
OF EACH CATEGORY!
WHAT WOULD THE
CATEGORIES BE?

E.g. The award for
BEST FRIEND
goes to me!

Who would present the awards?

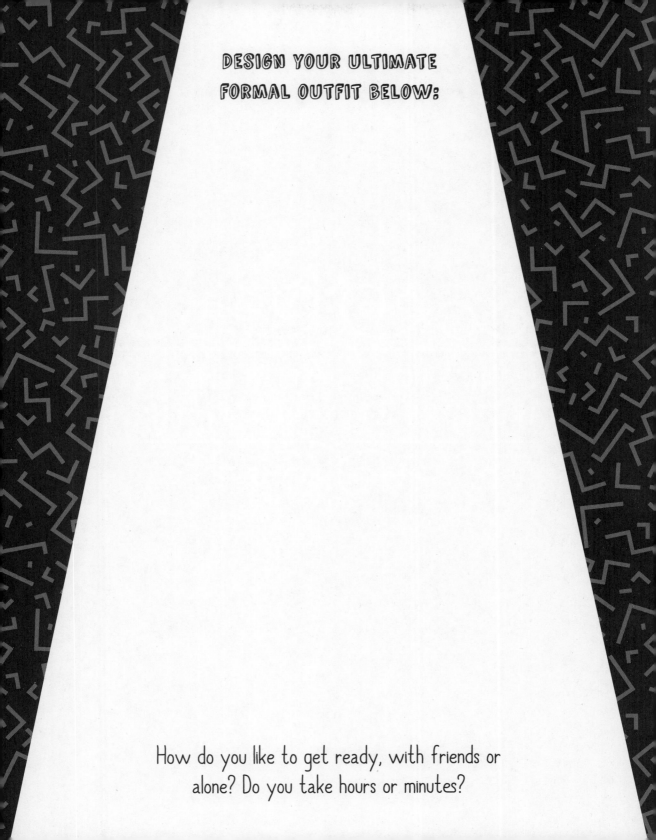

DESIGN YOUR ULTIMATE FORMAL OUTFIT BELOW:

How do you like to get ready, with friends or alone? Do you take hours or minutes?

YOU CAN'T POUR FROM AN EMPTY CUP.
TAKE CARE OF YOURSELF FIRST.

ARE YOU A GLASS HALF FULL OR A
GLASS HALF EMPTY KIND OF A PERSON?

DRAW SEVEN GLASSES BELOW,
AND MARK DOWN HOW FULL OR EMPTY
YOU FEEL ON DIFFERENT DAYS.

CAN YOU THINK
OF A FEW WAYS
TO GET YOUR
GLASS FULL?

MUSICAL MOMENT

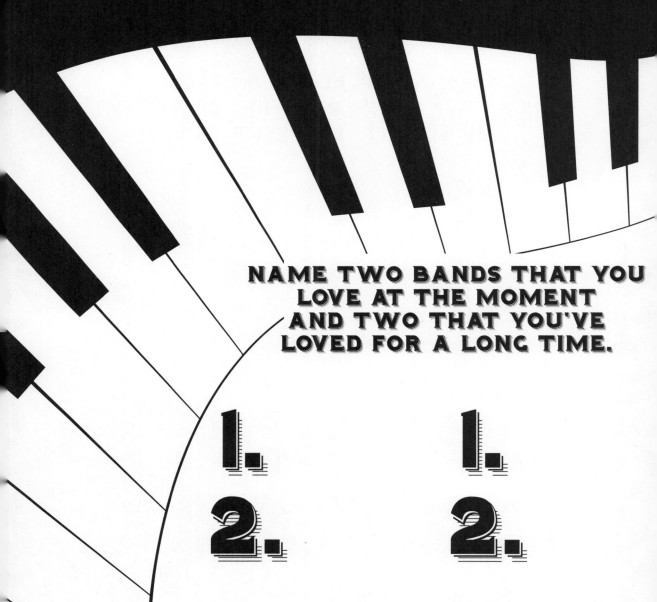

NAME TWO BANDS THAT YOU LOVE AT THE MOMENT AND TWO THAT YOU'VE LOVED FOR A LONG TIME.

1.

2.

1.

2.

Make your own band out of you and the special people in your life.

WHO'S THE LEAD SINGER?

....

WHO'S ON THE DRUMS?

....

WHO ARE THE BACKGROUND DANCERS?

....

WHICH ROLE DO YOU PLAY?

....

DRAW OUT YOUR BAND AND THEN WRITE DOWN THE BAND'S NAME ON A POSTER OR THE DRUM KIT.

WHICH ACTOR WOULD PLAY YOU IN THE FILM OF YOUR LIFE? FOR WHAT REASONS? WHAT MAKES THEM AS AMAZING AS YOU?

WHICH ACTORS WOULD PLAY SOME OF YOUR LOVED ONES?

IN THE STYLE OF AN ACTOR YOU ADMIRE, GRAB YOUR PHONE AND TAKE A SELFIE HEADSHOT. SKETCH A COPY BELOW AND NOTE DOWN ALL THE THINGS THAT YOU LOVE ABOUT IT.

> "
>
> Do what you love and love what you do
>
> "

If love was a scene, what would it look like?

What things would it have in it?

If love was an animal, what would it be?

Would it have a name?

If love was an action, what would it be?

"HOLDING ONTO ANGER IS LIKE GRASPING A HOT COAL WITH THE INTENTION OF THROWING IT AT SOMEONE ELSE. YOU'RE THE ONE GETTING BURNED." BUDDHA.

IN OTHER WORDS: LET IT GO.

Have a let-it-go brain dump all over this page, writing down anything that you need to free your mind from. Don't think too much and just write.

SOME WAYS TO LET GO ARE:

1. Create a mantra to remind yourself of the good.

2. Accept that you may never get the result you want.

3. Mental and physical distance.

4. Self-care and self-love.

WHAT OTHER WAYS CAN YOU THINK OF?

RATE THESE ACTIVITIES OUT OF TEN.

GOING SHOPPING

1 2 3 4 5 6 7 8 9 10

TAKING A BATH

1 2 3 4 5 6 7 8 9 10

READING A BOOK

1 2 3 4 5 6 7 8 9 10

SEEING FRIENDS

1 2 3 4 5 6 7 8 9 10

GOING FOR A WALK

1 2 3 4 5 6 7 8 9 10

BEING ALONE

1 2 3 4 5 6 7 8 9 10

GOING TO BED EARLY

1 2 3 4 5 6 7 8 9 10

HAVING ME-TIME

1 2 3 4 5 6 7 8 9 10

WHICH OF THE ACTIVITIES SCORED EIGHT OR ABOVE? CREATE A WEEKLY PLAN BELOW AND INCORPORATE PLENTY OF THESE HIGH-RANKING ACTIVITIES INTO YOUR WEEK.

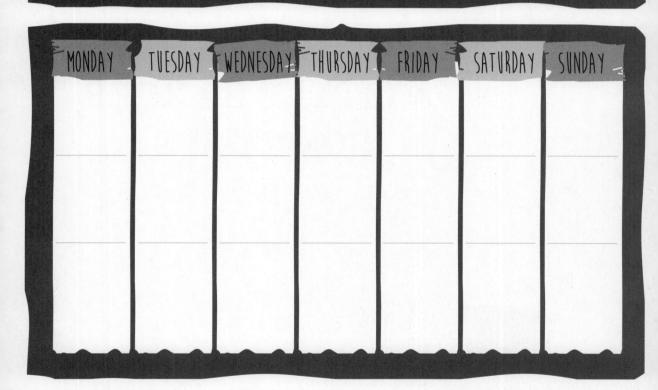

MONDAY	TUESDAY	WEDNESDAY	THURSDAY	FRIDAY	SATURDAY	SUNDAY

THINK ABOUT ANY LOW-RANKING ONES. WHAT COULD BE DONE TO MAKE THEM RANK HIGHER FOR YOU?

LOOK FOR SOMETHING POSITIVE IN EACH DAY, EVEN IF YOU HAVE TO LOOK A LITTLE HARDER SOME DAYS.

Write ten things that make you feel truly positive.

1. _____
2. _____
3. _____
4. _____
5. _____
6. _____
7. _____
8. _____
9. _____
10. _____

MY DREAM DIARY

Describe a dream you've had recently:

What do you think it means?

Do you dream often?

Do you tend to remember your dreams?

Are there common themes to your dreams?

Sleep dreams happen without your control,
but now write down five dreams in your control
that you would like to achieve.

1.

2.

3.

4.

5.

TAKE A PAUSE TO BE IN THE
PRESENT. ANSWER THE QUESTIONS
BELOW TO GROUND YOURSELF
AND TO BE TRULY AWARE OF
YOUR SURROUNDINGS.

Where are you?

What can you see around you?

What can you smell?

What can you hear?

How do you feel?

Write down something
that's on your mind:

NOW YOU'RE GROUNDED AND IN THE MOMENT, CREATE A DIY GUIDED MEDITATION BELOW. CHOOSE A RELAXING SETTING AND DESCRIBE EVERYTHING ABOUT IT, AND HOW ALL OF YOUR SENSES AND EMOTIONS ARE REACTING TO IT.

E.g. I'm imagining myself on a warm beach. I can hear the gentle surf and the crunch of the sand under my feet. A gentle breeze brushes past me. I feel calm and content.

FALL THREE TIMES;
STAND UP FOUR.

Think of three ways of showing kindness to your friend:

1
2
3

Now, three ways to show kindness to a stranger:

1
2
3

Now, three ways to show kindness to yourself:

1
2
3

WHAT ARE YOUR WORK GOALS FOR THIS WEEK?

....

....

....

....

....

....

....

NOW, PLAN SOME WORK GOALS FOR THE NEXT FIVE YEARS:

....

....

....

....

....

....

....

What are your fun goals FOR THIS WEEK?

....
....
....
....
....
....
....

Now, plan some fun goals FOR THE NEXT FIVE YEARS:

....
....
....
....
....
....
....

Use this double page to think about everything you've learned as you've gone through this journal.

What have I learned about myself? ....
....
....
....
....
....

Why am I amazing? ....
....
....
....
....
....
....

What makes a person amazing? ....
....
....
....
....
....
....

The quote that meant the most to me was: ....
....
....
....
....
....

Some kind things I can say about myself: ....
....
....
....
....
....
....

Some kind things I can do for other people: ....
....
....
....
....
....
....

My personal affirmation: : ....
....

YOU ARE AWESOME. YOU HAVE THE ABILITY TO DO AWESOME THINGS.

WITH THAT IN MIND, WRITE DOWN AND SKETCH LOTS OF LITTLE WAYS THAT YOU CAN BRING SOME SUNSHINE, SOME POSITIVITY, SOME AWESOME-NESS INTO YOUR AND YOUR LOVED ONES' LIVES.

"YOU'RE EVEN MORE AMAZING THAN YOU THINK YOU ARE"